Principles of Supervision Learning Guide

Principles of
SUPERVISION

TABLE OF CONTENTS

Learning Objectives & Outcomes

At the end of this two-day workshop, you will able to:

- Describe the core responsibilities and role of a supervisor
- Establish goals and set standards that raise employee performance
- Coach employees on performance
- Lead development discussions with high-performing employees
- Diagnose reasons for performance problems and how to address them
- Personalize the approach you use to motivate employees
- Take steps to increase employee engagement
- Describe how the basic functions of management impact goal achievement
- Delegate to help employees develop confidence and expand their skills
- Describe where you need to focus your relationship building efforts
- Promote communication by role-modeling three essential skills
- Take actions to foster and improve teamwork
- Describe how your personality traits impact behavior
- Develop supervision skills more efficiently and effectively

Module One

Introduction

Principles of
SUPERVISION

Supervisory Skills Framework

In higher education, we often seem to focus less on good supervision, and more on the glamorous and exciting work of leadership.

However, supervisors are responsible for making sure that things are done properly. And while leaders may bring us vision, inspiration, and challenge, these things count for nothing without the efficient implementation brought about by good supervision.

To be a great supervisor, you must have an extensive set of skills—from planning and delegation to communication and motivation. Because the skill set is so wide, it's tempting to build skills in the areas of management that you're already comfortable with. But for your long-term success, it's wise to analyze your skills in all areas of supervision, and then to challenge yourself to improve in *all* of these areas.

Managing
PERFORMANCE

Developing
DIRECT REPORTS

Guiding & Organizing
THE WORK

Managing
RELATIONSHIPS

Managing
YOURSELF

Role of the Supervisor

To create a safe, productive, motivating work environment where people take responsibility for their jobs and themselves, they develop their critical thinking skills, and you lead by example.

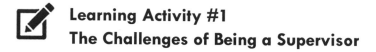

Learning Activity #1
The Challenges of Being a Supervisor

It is likely that you are in this position because you were a superior performer in your area of expertise. Being a supervisor, however, demands different skills. Let's explore some of the differences.

Take two minutes to write just one answer under each of the following questions:

1. What are the major differences between being an individual contributor and being a supervisor?

2. What is rewarding about this role?

3. What uncertainties or concerns do you have about your role as supervisor?

The Difference between Leadership and Management

You Are a Leader and a Manager

"Your foremost job as a leader is to take charge of your own energy and then to help orchestrate the energy of those around you."   Peter F. Drucker

How Leadership and Management Differ

In John Kotter's 1990 book *A Force for Change – How Leadership Differs from Supervision/Management,* he draws a distinction between management and leadership.

Kotter summarizes what he considers to be the important leadership processes:

1. **Establishing Direction**

   • Developing a vision of the future, often the distant future, along with strategies for producing changes needed to achieve that vision

2. **Aligning People**

   • Communicating direction so that people understand the vision and their role in achieving it

   • Building coalitions to foster cooperation and collective pursuit of the vision

3. **Motivating and Inspiring**

   • Driving people in the right direction in spite of political, bureaucratic, and resource-based barriers to change

   • Appealing to basic, but often untapped, human needs, values, and emotions

Kotter summarizes the classic supervision/managerial processes as follows:

1. **Planning and Budgeting**
   - Setting targets or goals for the future, typically the next month or year
   - Establishing detailed steps, timetables and guidelines for achieving targets
   - Allocating resources to accomplish targets and execute on plans

2. **Organizing and Staffing**
   - Establishing an organizational structure and set of jobs for accomplishing plan requirements
   - Staffing jobs with qualified individuals
   - Communicating the plan to those people, delegating responsibility for carrying out the plan
   - Establishing systems to monitor implementation

3. **Controlling and Problem-solving**
   - Monitoring results against plan (both formally and informally) through reports, meetings, etc.
   - Identifying deviations (or "problems")
   - Planning and organizing to solve those problems

The Balance between Leadership and Management

LEADERS	MANAGERS
• Focus on vision and strategy	• Focus on operations
• Appeal to the heart	• Appeal to the head
• Lead people	• Manage work
• Influence and inspire	• Give detail and directions
• Have followers	• Have subordinates
• Ask questions	• Formulate detail
• Embrace risk and change	• Sustain the status quo
• Accountable to the organization	• Accountable to the team

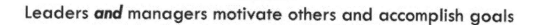

Leaders **and** managers motivate others and accomplish goals

Learning Activity #2
Handling Change as a Leader or Manager

The California State University system has decided to implement a single systemwide Human Resources Management System this year. This change will impact your campus and your day-to-day process related to timekeeping, recruiting, and other ongoing activities.

For the past few years, your campus used its own system and dictated its own processes. With this change, there will be less process and systems flexibility. It will, however, create synergies to the CSU as a system and save a lot of tax payer money.

Some campuses will benefit from this change via new features and support they did not have in the past while other campuses might lose functionality.

1. Using the following three leader characteristics, write what you would say as a leader to your team about these changes.

To ...	I would say ...
Appeal to their hearts	
Ask questions and get their thoughts	
Influence and inspire	

2. After writing your talking points, practice delivering them with a partner.

Module Two

Managing Performance and Developing Direct Reports

What is Performance Management?

What Is Performance Management?

Performance management is the process by which supervisors and employees work together to plan, monitor, and review an employee's work objectives and overall contributions to the work unit. It is essential for helping your university achieve its mission and strategic goals. As a supervisor, your ability to manage performance is dependent on three conditions:

- Understanding of the system and the environment in which you work

- Knowledge of the people who work for you

- Ability to manage employees for various situations

Performance Management Pre-work

Before conducting performance management meetings with employees, supervisors should:

- Have a clear understanding of the university's mission and vision

- Know the work unit's mission, vision, and goals

- Have updated job descriptions and performance expectations for each employee

- Be familiar with development areas noted on each employee's previous performance reviews

Performance Management Steps

- Plan the Work and Set Expectations

- Observe Individual Performance

- Develop the Capacity to Perform

- Evaluate Performance

- Recognize Successful Performance

Plan Work and Set Expectations

Define Job-Specific Performance Standards

What Are Performance Standards?

- Measures that provide employees with specific expectations for the tasks that make up each job duty

- This information provides the foundation for assessing performance

- Performance standards help employees better understand the work to be accomplished, and the minimal level of **acceptable** performance

Guidelines

To be effective, performance standards should include three components:

1. A clear description of work to be accomplished
2. Details on how performance will be measured (quantity, cost, timeliness)
3. An indication of expected level of success

Task + Measurement + Expected Level of Success = *Performance Standard*

Challenges

- Not all job functions can be easily broken down into tasks
- Measurement - some tasks (such as transactional tasks) are easier to measure while others (such as interpersonal or soft skills) are harder.

"One of the most powerful drivers of performance within a performance management system comes from employees having a clear understanding of performance standards." Corporate Leadership Council

Examples of Performance Standards

Job	Job Duty	Task / Work to be Accomplished	+ Expected Level of Success	+ Measurement	= Performance Standard
Office and Administrative Specialist	Office Support	Open Financial Aid office.	promptly	at 8:00am	Open Financial Aid office promptly at 8:00am
	Preparation of Materials	Assemble training materials.	accurately	within two working of days request	Accurately assemble training materials within two working days of request.
Library Assistant	Customer Service	Respond to library patrons' questions.	clear focus on customer service	within a minute	Respond to library patrons' questions within a minute, with clear focus on customer service.
	Monitor Borrowing	Contact library users for return of books and materials.	using overdue notice email template	once per day or shift	Contact library users for return of books and materials using overdue notice email template.
Admissions Representative	Student Enrollment	Process grad school applications.	accurately	25 per day	Accurately process 25 applications for grad school per day.
	Relationship Management	Establish relationships with students, families, and communities served by College.	maintain positive relationships	5 outreach calls per full-time day	Establish and maintain positive relationships with students, families, and communities through regular contact (5 calls per day).
Food Service Supervisor	Inventory Control	Accept deliveries of food shipments and inventory them.	in person	within two working days	Accept deliveries of food shipments from vendors in person, inventory them within two working days of delivery.

Job	Job Duty	Task / Work to be Accomplished	+ Expected Level of Success	+ Measurement	= Performance Standard
Food Service Supervisor (continued)	Scheduling	Schedule and coordinate staffing of student employees.	ensure proper coverage	weekly	Schedule and coordinate staffing of student employees on weekly basis to ensure proper coverage.
IT Support Desk Manager	Software Upgrades	Oversee installation of Microsoft software upgrades.	with minimal interruption to users	timing based on each upgrade project plan	Oversee installation of Microsoft software upgrades with minimal interruption to users.
	Performance Management	Provide performance feedback to Support Desk employees.	accurate, specific	bi-weekly	Provide accurate, specific performance feedback to Support Desk employees.
Psychology Professor	Teaching	Teach undergraduate Social Psychology courses.	use innovative instructional methods, techniques, and materials	16 weeks per semester including, at a minimum, a mid-term and final exam	Use innovative instructional methods, techniques, and materials to teach under-graduate Social Psychology courses.
	Advising	Help undergraduate students achieve their academic goals.	provide knowledgeable and skilled guidance	10 advisory meetings per semester	Provide knowledgeable, skilled guidance so under-graduate students achieve academic goals.

Learning Activity #3a
Setting Performance Standards

In this activity, you will practice writing performance standards for at least one member of your team.

1. Write down one job duty of an employee who reports to you.
2. List the tasks that make up that job duty.
3. Develop performance standards for each task.

Job	Job Duty	Task / Work to be Accomplished	+ Expected Level of Success	+ Measurement	= Performance Standard

Learning Activity #3b
Setting Performance Standards

After everyone in your group has shared, discuss these questions:

1. Two different supervisors in the same department supervising employees who do the exact same work may set different performance standards. What are some reasons for these differences?

2. What are some steps supervisors could take to avoid having different performance standards for the same job?

Establish Behavioral Expectations for Team

Which Behavioral Expectations are Important

Most performance problems encountered by supervisors are not related to their employee's ability to successfully carry out job duties or tasks, but rather to interpersonal skills or behavior. In spite of that, when an employee joins an organization, much more time is spent reviewing job duties and tasks than behaviors that will lead to employee and team success. One of your key responsibilities is to establish behavioral expectations that will contribute to team success.

Learning Activity #4
Defining Behavioral Expectations

Read the following then discuss the questions on the following page.

While attending University X, I got a job as a child care worker in the College of Education's Child Development Center. The center was a training site for early development and childcare with research opportunities to further knowledge of early development, education, and quality care for young children.

I showed up for my first day of work on Monday and was given a tour of the building and went over my job description with the Center Director. On Friday, my fifth day of work, I looked out the window at the playground and noticed two other child care workers picking up toys and sports equipment to put away in the storage room. It looked like there were enough people to handle the task so I continued working at my desk.

Without even knowing it, I had violated a basic unwritten rule of the center: everyone helps clean up at the end of the day. It was a symbol of the teamwork necessary to make the center function well. You see, teamwork is a big issue when working with small children because their safety and well-being is paramount.

The next two weeks were quite unpleasant as nasty looks, sarcastic comments, and terse exchanges were common. I finally summoned the courage to ask what was going on, and was told of my mistake.

1. Which behavioral expectations could be put in place to prevent others from experiencing what this person went through?

2. What could you do to determine behaviors that would help all employees contribute to the Child Development Center's success? Who should be involved in this process?

3. Once behavioral expectations have been set, who should communicate them to new employees and how should they be communicated?

Recognizing and Rating Northwestern Behaviors

Working in the area of performance excellence and assessment over the past several years, staff in Northwestern Human Resources have identified "Northwestern behaviors." These are desired behaviors that are consistent with Northwestern's goals and that if developed by employees, will help make the University an even better place to work, learn, and live.

True success in the workplace depends both on **what** we accomplish and **how** we get things done. In the Performance Excellence Process:

- **What** we accomplish are **performance objectives**
- **How** we accomplish things are **Northwestern behaviors**

Employees of Northwestern University are encouraged to demonstrate the following behaviors in order to successfully accomplish their performance objectives.

- **Coachability:** Being receptive to feedback; willing to learn; embracing continuous improvement.

- **Collegiality:** Being helpful, respectful, approachable, and team oriented; building strong working relationships and a positive work environment.

- **Communication:** Balancing listening and talking; speaking and writing clearly and accurately; influencing others; keeping others informed.

- **Compliance:** Honoring University policies and regulatory requirements.

- **Customer focus:** Striving for high customer satisfaction; going out of the way to be helpful and pleasant; making it as easy as possible for the customer (rather than the department or the University).

- **Efficiency:** Planning ahead; managing time well; being on time; being cost-conscious; thinking of better ways to do things.

- **Initiative:** Taking ownership of work; doing what is needed without being asked; following through.

- **Leadership (as applicable):** Setting clear expectations; reviewing progress; providing feedback and guidance; holding people accountable.

Detailed examples of these behaviors—outstanding, effective, and needs improvement—follow.

Recognizing and Rating Northwestern Behaviors

Coachability

Needs Improvement	Effective	Outstanding
Asks for little feedback from others on development needs and progress	Solicits feedback from customers, peers, and superiors, and uses this information to develop know-how and self-awareness	Uses feedback from others to make noticeable and noteworthy changes in his/her skills and productivity
Does not show an interest in learning new skills, technologies, and workplace trends	Displays curiosity and seeks opportunities to master new skills and knowledge	Anticipates learning needs and has a plan in place to meet those needs
Does not share learning resources or expertise with others	Shares learning resources and expertise (articles, web pages, books, professional contacts) with others to strengthen their knowledge	Known for valuing learning; finds time and space for helping others learn
Tries to cover up mistakes	Learns from mistakes	Shows team members how mistakes can be valuable learning opportunities
Has few or no goals/objectives for professional development	Sets achievable, challenging goals/objectives for professional development	Has a professional development plan to address ongoing short- and long-term learning needs
Needs more awareness of professional information that affects the University and his/her job	Keeps current on professional information that affects the University and his/her job	Anticipates major functional changes that affect his/her job and takes steps to prepare for them
Rarely takes part in developmental activities outside the workplace	Takes steps to improve expertise by joining professional organizations and participating in conferences and training as appropriate	Participates in leadership roles in professional organizations and conferences

Recognizing and Rating Northwestern Behaviors

Collegiality

Needs Improvement	Effective	Outstanding
Acts as if own ideas and opinions are "the final word" and minimizes or ignores the team's contributions	Values the insights and thinking that can be achieved by a team	Actively supports and implements team decisions and ideas, and gives full credit to the team for successful outcomes
Most comfortable with team members who are similar to him/her	Interacts comfortably and effectively with other team members	Makes special efforts to ensure that all team members are respectful of one another and work together productively
Ignores or works against team decisions	Seeks group participation and consensus	Actively supports and implements team decisions
Displays behaviors that create conflict on the team	Displays behaviors that reduce team conflicts	Mediates and helps the team resolve team conflicts
Prefers to work alone and is reluctant to participate in team activities	Participates actively in group meetings and team-building activities	Volunteers enthusiastically to work on intra- and inter-departmental teams
Has difficulty building relationships to accomplish results	Uses formal and informal approaches to develop and build effective working relationships within and outside his/her own group, and with multiple levels of the organization	Influences others who are not under his/her direct authority or control to accomplish results
Needs to show more sensitivity to the diversity of coworkers and internal and external customers	Relates well to others in the organization who differ in status, age, race, religion, gender, or disability	Adjusts interpersonal approaches to attend to the needs of diverse groups of people
Tends to get locked into his/her own way of looking at issues	Remains open to others' points of view, even when they conflict with his/her own	Negotiates with others to reach a win-win outcome

Recognizing and Rating Northwestern Behaviors

Communication

Needs Improvement	Effective	Outstanding
Interrupts others; does not listen attentively; comes across as condescending	Demonstrates respect for others by listening actively; demonstrates appropriate nonverbal behaviors; verifies understanding	Encourages and values input; shows an interest in others' needs and concerns even when under pressure
Fails to share pertinent information	Shares (accurate) information openly and honestly and in a timely and assertive fashion	Anticipates communication needs and shares information effectively with all levels of the organization
Speaks unclearly, which prompts recipients to ask for clarification	Speaks clearly; avoids vagueness, ambiguity, and mixed messages; demonstrates appropriate nonverbal behaviors	Promotes and uses candid and open speaking style
Written communication often contains errors	Presents facts and ideas accurately and clearly in writing	Notes and reports are often forwarded and cited
People tend to "tune out" this person during discussions	Proposes ideas persuasively in oral communication	People often enjoy listening to this person talk and are influenced by him/her
Uses oral communication when written would be more appropriate — and vice versa	Uses appropriate communication channels and length depending on message and audience	Uses exactly the right medium (e-mail, voice mail, in person) at just the right length depending on message and audience
Shares confidential information with inappropriate parties	Maintains confidence as appropriate	Sought after as a confidant
Demonstrates passive or aggressive verbal and/or non-verbal behaviors during conflict	Demonstrates assertive verbal and/or non-verbal behaviors during conflict	Resolves conflicts and opens lines of communication

Recognizing and Rating Northwestern Behaviors

Compliance

Needs Improvement	Effective	Outstanding
Cannot explain consequences of non-compliance	Strives for full compliance	Seeks continual compliance improvements
Does not consider compliance in daily work and decisions	Identifies methods for achieving compliance	Uncovers and corrects causes of non-compliance
Bends the rules and "asks for forgiveness"	Follows University and regulatory policies/requirements unless exceptions are necessary and pre-approved	Sought after by colleagues and "strangers" who want to know the correct way to do things
Does not comply with standardized processes and procedures	Complies with standardized processes and procedures	Has obtained appropriate certifications in work process improvement techniques

Recognizing and Rating Northwestern Behaviors

Customer Focus

Needs Improvement	Effective	Outstanding
Displays less than friendly and helpful behaviors toward customers	Demonstrates, with both verbal and non-verbal behaviors, a warm and friendly demeanor toward customers	Noted for displaying customer service behaviors that exceed customers' expectations
Rarely listens to or solicits feedback from internal or external customers	Solicits and acts on customer feedback	Visits or calls customers to find out what they are doing and what they need; stays abreast of developments that may be relevant to them
Slow to respond to customer needs	Responds to customer needs while adhering to departmental service-level standards and time frames	Frequently exceeds agreed-upon service levels and time frames
Does not admit to or recover from customer mistakes as quickly as desired	Admits to customer mistakes and corrects them quickly	Learns from customer mistakes so that they are not repeated in future interactions
Has few or no methods in place to track customer satisfaction	Has qualitative and quantitative mechanisms to track customer satisfaction	Works with other team members to find better qualitative and quantitative ways to track customer satisfaction
Sees difficult customers as obstacles beyond his/her control	Views difficult customers as opportunities to improve self, processes, and or products	Seeks out customer problems and complaints and removes barriers that get in the way of meeting and exceeding customer needs

Recognizing and Rating Northwestern Behaviors

Efficiency

Needs Improvement	Effective	Outstanding
Arrives late and/or unprepared for work	Begins work on time/prepared; schedules non-work activities outside of work hours	Known for exceptional attendance record
Takes unusually long time or extra effort to complete regular work	Manages time well; delivers expected results with reasonable time and effort	Produces extraordinary results while rarely working overtime and without "working too hard"
Not conscientious about spending or accounting for department funds; does not work within budget	Conscientious about spending and accounting for department funds; works within budget	Conscientious about spending and accounting for department funds. Finds ways to save and recover money
Has a minimal understanding of key work processes in department and/or area	Understands key work processes in department and/or area and uses them effectively	Continuously strives to improve key work processes
Rarely applies quality or process improvement techniques within his/her functional area	Consistently applies process improvement techniques to work to improve quality and/or efficiency	Identifies benchmarks with others to find process improvement opportunities
Does not consistently measure the effect of process improvements	Measures quality improvements in his/her own work area or process and reports them to management	Helps others to develop measures for quality improvements in their own work areas

Recognizing and Rating Northwestern Behaviors

Initiative

Needs Improvement	Effective	Outstanding
Requires close supervision, even on routine assignments	Performs work independently without being asked; takes ownership and follows through	Significantly exceeds expectations by doing more than is required and by initiating and implementing new projects
Operates in reactive mode; often does things only when asked	Anticipates problems; proactively addresses issues	Recognizes and seizes opportunities even if outside of normal job duties
Misses deadlines; often requests extensions	Meets deadlines	Pursues solutions to problems with a sense of urgency; beats deadlines
Adheres to ineffective methods after being asked to change	Generates innovative ideas, approaches, and solutions	Ideas are adopted by the department or the University
Fails to meet basic responsibilities	Fulfills all primary responsibilities	Seeks new challenges and secondary responsibilities
Does not help others beyond regular job responsibilities	Looks for extra ways to help colleagues and customers	Formally recognized for going "above and beyond the call of duty" (thank you notes, Northwestern Service Excellence awards)
Takes little or no action when things go wrong	Offers to help work toward solutions when things go wrong	Takes charge and finds solutions when things go wrong
Cannot always be trusted to follow through	Earns trust by doing what he/she says will be done	Always does what he/she says will be done; is noted for trustworthiness and dependability

Recognizing and Rating Northwestern Behaviors

Leadership
(as applicable)

Needs Improvement	Effective	Outstanding
Has no mission or communicates mission unclearly to team members	Communicates a clear, compelling mission to team members and motivates them to achieve that mission	Motivates others in the organization to achieve mission
Does not use the Performance Excellence Process to enhance employee performance	Uses the Performance Excellence Process to set expectations, coach employees, and conduct annual performance reviews	Champions the Performance Excellence Process and uses it successfully to increase productivity and develop employees
Makes the majority of important team decisions	Encourages and supports team decision making and problem solving	Helps team develop more collaborative and productive ways of problem solving and decision making
Insensitive in dealing with employee mistakes or failures	Motivates others to perform by providing constructive and timely feedback	Encourages employee growth and achievement by emphasizing learning from mistakes and failures and building on successes
Viewed as uncomfortable, closed, or withholding when communicating	Communicates openly, honestly, and comfortably with others	Teaches staff better ways of communicating with customers, peers, and each other
Has a history of not selecting the right candidates for the job and/or not thoroughly orienting them	Selects the right people based on the candidate's past experiences, successes, and fit to the area's culture. Orients them to their jobs	Assesses talent well; people want to work with him/her

Learning Activity #5
Behavioral Expectations

Think of an individual who reports to you. Using the definitions on page 15 and the behavior refinements on pages 16-23, describe his/her rating on behavioral expectations.

How do you know? Why would you use that rating? Be specific.

Direct Report	Needs Improvement	Effective	Outstanding
Coachability			
Collegiality			
Communication			
Compliance			
Customer Focus			
Efficiency			
Initiative			
Leadership (as applicable)			

Further, determine if your employee requires training or orientation *before* starting the work. If so, decide how the learning transfer can best take place. Ways in which your employee can learn include work experience, on-the-job training (OJT), learning from others, and learning through online or instructor-led training.

Action Plan
Behavioral Expectation Ideas

1.   Meet with your manager and get their input.

2.   Check with HR to see if this work has been done already. Does your
        university or work unit have a competency model or list of success
        factors?

3.   Find out behaviors that are important to your team's success.

- Use your own experience

- Ask your clients or customers

- Industry or function best practices

- Ask peers on other campuses

- Get input from employees

Your Action Plan

When you complete a formal learning event or informal development activity:

1. Take some time (a minimum of five minutes) to brainstorm a list of your insights.

2. Ask yourself: What do I want to do as a result of this new information and/or these insights?

3. Tell your manager about your plans.
   If they aren't available, find an "accountability buddy" or someone who knows and will follow up with you — in other words, someone who'll help you stick to it.

   Your boss or accountability buddy can help improve learning transfer by guiding your action planning efforts:

   • Ask them to hold you accountable

   • Explain what you learned

   • Review what you will do differently as a result

   • Ask them to follow up with you and check on your progress

 Action Plan
Ideas for your Action Plan

1. Thinking about what you've learned so far, which skills do you plan to develop?

2. What are your major steps and milestone due dates?

3. What resources will you need to move forward with your skills development?

4. When will you have substantially improved your skills?

5. Who is your accountability buddy?

Accountability Buddies

Successful execution of your Action Plan is partially based in developing an accountability buddy - someone you trust and with whom you share your Action Plan, successes and obstacles.

Your accountability buddy provides ideas and constructive feedback to you. Further, you can provide that same 'sounding board' for them.

Here are some ideas for the structure of your accountability buddy discussions:

- *Define the frequency and length of each meeting. For example, once a week for one hour.*

- *Share with your accountability buddy up to three situations you are dealing with in your department.*

- *Ask your buddy which tools from this training would be helpful to use in those situations.*

- *Discuss how to apply the tools, what approach to use.*

- *Practice conversations if needed.*

- *Review progress on your Action Plan.*

- *Then switch.*

Observe Individual Performance

Observing individual performance is crucial in order to fairly, objectively, and effectively coach for better performance, increased skills, and recognition of jobs well done. It's done throughout the year, not just only before evaluation time.

Observing individual performance is time-consuming on the supervisor's part, but investing this time will allow you to discover the strengths and growth areas of your employees. It will also ensure your business processes are working as they should.

Ways to Collect Performance Information

The easiest way to collect information is to directly watch the employee's performance. It might be helpful, however, if you watch in an informal way rather than a formal one as it's less intimidating.

Listen to others' comments about the employee's performance. Contact stakeholders who have interactions with your employee and find out what is working and what could use some improvement. Perhaps a client or stakeholder has sent them a thank you note? Those are extremely helpful when creating the full picture of performance.

In each case – direct observation and stakeholder comments – take specific, objective, written notes of behavior, dates, times, and circumstances in which the performance occurred.

Barriers to Effective Performance Depictions

Everyone has their biases. Biases come from our experiences, both personal and professional. However, when evaluating performance, these biases must be put aside so that a fair and objective performance description will be given.

Here are some bias barriers to avoid:

Contrast	This occurs when a supervisor compares an employee's performance to other employees instead of the standard. When employees are ranked in comparison, someone must end up at the bottom, even if they are exceeding the standard.
Halo	An employee is rated highly in all areas because of one thing they do really well. For example, a sales person might hit the numbers and impress senior leadership, but behind the scenes, create havoc and lose the respect of co-workers.
Horns	On the flip side, an employee is rated as a poor performer because of one thing they don't do well. For example, the administrative assistant who is great at everything except filing. It piles up because they put it off, which results in the company hiring a temp to get caught up on filing. In all other areas, they're a rock star.
Leniency	A manager gives everyone on their team a satisfactory rating. This can happen when managers have a large span of control coupled with a common review date. Faced with so many reviews to write, the manager gets burned out and gives everyone a satisfactory response because it doesn't require any written supporting statements.
Recency	The employee's most recent behavior becomes the primary focus of the review. This can go both ways. A poor performer does something terrific and their past performance is forgotten. Or an excellent performer makes a mistake and it weighs down the rest of the review.
Gender	Read the following report to learn how significantly unconscious bias can directly affect women's career success and advancement.

Women in the Workplace - A Special Report

Managers: Watch Your Language: Research suggests that unconscious gender bias affects workplace feedback and advancement
Author: Silverman, Rachel Emma

Abstract

When participants in corporate workshops about unconscious bias are asked which of two candidates they would pick to replace a top performer in their organization, about 90% select the person described in terms related to individual initiative - the same words that turned up more often in the men's performance reviews in the Stanford study, Dr. Simard says.

Full text

If companies are looking for gender bias in their workplace, here's one place they may want to start: feedback.

Research suggests that men and women are assessed very differently at work. Specifically, managers are significantly more likely to critique female employees for coming on too strong, and their accomplishments are more likely than men's to be seen as the result of team, rather than individual efforts, finds new research from Stanford University's Clayman Institute for Gender Research. Those trends appear to hold up whether the boss making the assessments is male or female.

The researchers say the differences are products of unconscious bias - hidden beliefs about women's capabilities that can influence important workplace decisions. For instance, if bosses expect women to be more team-oriented and men to be more independent in their jobs, women may be more likely to be shunted into support roles rather than landing the core positions that lead to executive jobs, the researchers say. Many employees internalize these stereotypes over time, they add, sapping some women's confidence that they or their female co-workers can handle more demanding positions.

"Stereotypes shape our perceptions of competence. We hold women to a higher standard in evaluations, and women also tend to evaluate themselves to a higher bar," says Caroline Simard, director of research at the Clayman Institute. Such hidden biases could ultimately lead to "cumulative disadvantage over a woman's

career over time, resulting in lower access to key leadership positions and stretch assignments, advancement and pay," she says.

The Stanford team is analyzing the language of hundreds of performance reviews from four technology and professional-services firms. The research is continuing, but so far it has shown that women received 2.5 times the amount of feedback men did about aggressive communication styles, with phrases such as "your speaking style is off-putting," the study found. Women were described as "supportive," "collaborative" and "helpful" nearly twice as often as men, and women's reviews had more than twice the references to team accomplishments, rather than individual achievements.

Men's reviews contained twice as many words related to assertiveness, independence and self-confidence -- words like "drive," "transform," "innovate" and "tackle." Men also received three times as much feedback linked to a specific business outcome, and twice the number of references to their technical expertise.

"The magnitude of some of the differences and how consistent they were across the different samples was shocking," Dr. Simard says.

Other research shows how such differences matter in promotions. When participants in corporate workshops about unconscious bias are asked which of two candidates they would pick to replace a top performer in their organization, about 90% select the person described in terms related to individual initiative -- the same words that turned up more often in the men's performance reviews in the Stanford study, Dr. Simard says.

Also, to outmaneuver those biases, women may spend more effort than men monitoring how they are perceived -- and that can take time away from getting work done, says Herminia Ibarra, a professor of organizational behavior at Instead, the business school in Fontainebleau, France.

"Too much focus on image and how you are being perceived is really counterproductive," she says.

Social scientists are still teasing out exactly why these gender biases persist and how to combat them. A big reason is that many companies use vague criteria, rather than specific measures, to evaluate employee performance, management researchers say.

But many companies are trying to do better, including Google Inc., Facebook Inc. and Dow Chemical Co., which have stepped up efforts to increase the numbers of women and minorities on their staffs. Microsoft Corp. now requires all employees to participate in an annual training program to educate them about unconscious bias.

For the past two years, cloud-computing firm VMware Inc. has been training employees and managers to recognize unconscious bias in their behaviors, says Betsy Sutter, the chief people officer of the Palo Alto, Calif., firm, which has some 18,000 employees world-wide, 22% of whom are women. In addition, before managers write up performance reviews, Ms. Sutter's team sends them a one-page memo reminding them about gender bias and potentially loaded phrases. For instance, the memo advises managers to avoid attributing women's contributions to external factors or luck.

Ms. Sutter says the guidelines have led to more awareness about gender bias, though it's too early to tell whether they've increased the number of women promoted.

Lisa Dalebout, a regional sales director at VMware, says she's now more careful of the language she uses with the seven employees who report directly to her, who are mostly men. She says she'll try to use the same language to describe the performance of both men and women. "I'm aware of it now, and you can't make the changes until you're aware," she says.

When Kieran Snyder worked as a manager at Microsoft, she received performance reviews that advised her to be less assertive, she says. "There was often an element of 'tone it down' in my reviews," says Dr. Snyder, who has a doctorate in linguistics. "I had one manager ask me explicitly to 'make room for others.' "

A Microsoft spokesman says: "We're committed to a diverse workforce and to a workplace where all employees have the chance to succeed."

Dr. Snyder says she never compared her reviews to those of her colleagues. But last year, after she left Microsoft, she decided to run her own linguistic analysis of performance reviews in the technology industry.

Over social media, she solicited a sample of 248 performance reviews of high-performing male and female employees from 28 tech companies. The results were similar to those of the Stanford study. Men were more likely to be given constructive suggestions related to specific skills, while women were more likely to get critical feedback to pipe down and be less aggressive. The manager's gender didn't seem to matter.

Those results led Dr. Snyder to cofound Textio Inc., a software company that analyzes language in job ads, aiming to help companies including Microsoft and Twitter Inc. avoid bias in job postings. Textio is also developing a performance-review product that sends prompts to managers if the language in a review appears to have gender biases.

"We want to help people before they make mistakes," says Dr. Snyder.

Ms. Silverman (rachel.silverman@wsj.com) is a Wall Street Journal reporter in Austin, Texas.

Loaded Language?

A study of performance reviews has found that compared with men, women receive:

2.5 TIMES
as much feedback about having an aggressive communication style

---

2.4 TIMES
as many references to team accomplishments

ABOUT HALF
as many references to their having vision

ABOUT HALF
as many references to their technical expertise

ONE THIRD
as much feedback linked to a business outcome

Source: Stanford University, Clayman Insitute for Gender Research
THE WALL STREET JOURNAL

Credit: By Rachel Emma Silverman
Publication title: Wall Street Jornal, Eastern edition
Publication year: 2015
Publication date: Sep 30, 2015
Place of publication: New York, NY
ISSN: 00999660

Develop the Capacity to Perform

Development Discussions

The research on employee engagement is clear: Employees with supervisors who regularly sit down with them to discuss professional development and career growth opportunities are more likely to stay and will work harder.

Different Types of Discussions

The Center for Creative Leadership (CCL) identifies four types of development discussions that supervisors might have with employees. The key is knowing enough about each employee's interests, skills, strengths, and weaknesses to have a constructive conversation. What would you say to an employee in each of these quadrants?

High +	Solid Performer Conversation	Top Talent Conversation
Performance	Underperformer Conversation	Potential Performer Conversation
Low −	**Potential**	High +

The Development Message

Consider the overall message you want to convey to an employee during a development conversation. That message will be different depending on your assessment of their performance and potential.

The four talent conversations below are designed to help you identify and simplify that message.

Employee	Message	Performance and Potential
Top talent	Future investment	Top talent are staff who clearly meet or exceed expectations and deliver superior results. These are individuals who are seen as future leaders in your department or university.
Solid performer	Maintaining or building value	Solid performers are typically individual contributors who are valued by your department or university, but who could take on more responsibility.
Potential performer	Short-term success	Potential performers are employees who may not have had enough time in their role to show significant results, but who are expected to bring a lot to the role they are in.
Under-performer	Improve performance	Underperformers are employees who are not meeting expectations and who need to improve to remain in their current role. These conversations should remain focused on here and now rather than future options, new tasks, or additional responsibilities.

*In a 2014 study, the Korn Ferry Institute identified **learning agility** as a top predictor of **performance potential**, noting that individuals with high learning agility are promoted twice as fast as those with low learning agility.*

Preparing for Development Discussions

1. Assess your department's or university's "development" needs. Based on strategy/vision/goals, what skills, knowledge, abilities, and experiences are needed from our talent?

2. Gather information and assess the individual, pulling together all data and information you have about this person.

   - What will be the key message conveyed during this development discussion? How do you anticipate the person will react?

   - To your knowledge, what motivates this person? What are this person's aspirations?

3. Consider next steps the person should focus on in terms of performance and development. Steps need to be based partially on your assessment of the individual, and more importantly based on what you hear and discuss during the actual discussion.

4. Identify next steps with the person

   - What developmental opportunities are available? What performance goals need to be met?

   - What will be the obstacles to development and performance?

5. Be prepared to identify ways to support this person. How a person perceives support is very individualized. Be careful not to define support in universal terms.

   - How will I help this person stay motivated? What resources can this person tap into besides me?

   - How will we create shared accountability for the person's development and performance?

Development Discussion Steps

1. Clarify purpose of the discussion.

2. Discuss strengths, vulnerabilities, developmental needs, and performance enhancement.

3. Generate opportunities for development or performance enhancement.

4. Set expectations about what needs to happen and by when.

5. Motivate by identifying meaningful goals and sources of support.

6. Identify the plan to stay on track and know when goals have been reached.

7. Ask the person to summarize what you agreed for next steps.

Use the 70/20/10 Framework When Developing New Skills

70% ON the Job - learning by experience

*   Assignments directly related to role
*   Assignments outside usual work responsibilities
*   Increased responsibilities in current role

20% NEAR the Job – learning from others

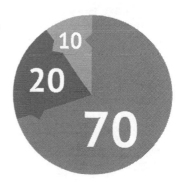

*   Feedback
*   Networking and conferences
*   Informal learning communities
*   Web-based research
*   Internal/external
*   Coaching/mentoring from experts

10% OFF the Job

*   Formal training courses or certifications

Evaluate Performance

The STAR/AR Coaching Model

STAR/AR is a coaching model designed to help you deliver feedback.

- Use the STAR section of the model to deliver positive feedback

- Use the full STAR/AR model to have a coaching dialog with employees and discuss constructive feedback

S T	Situation or Task	What was the performance challenge, opportunity or task?
A	Action	What did they say or do to meet / not meet the standard?
R	Result	What was the impact of their actions on you or others?
A	Alternate Action	What new action should be taken to reach a more effective result?
R	Enhanced Result	What is likely to occur as a result of taking the alternate action?

STAR/AR model used with permission of Development Dimensions International (DDI).

Example of Positive STAR Feedback

S T	Situation or Task	I really appreciate the initiative you took preparing for our weekly one-on-one meeting on Wednesday.
A	Action	You didn't wait for me to ask about the number of people who will need flu shots this year. You proactively found the data and sent it to me two days ahead of our meeting.
R	Result	Your data helped me answer some tough questions that the Director of the Student Health Center asked me on Tuesday.

Example of Constructive STAR/AR Feedback

Before discussing constructive feedback, use **positive intention** statements to set the tone and clearly indicate your intent to help your employees. For example:

- I'm committed to your success, and I have some feedback to help meet that commitment.

- I'd like to have a conversation so we are better aligned, and I have some feedback to accomplish that.

- Let's try to maximize your effectiveness in XYZ. I have feedback to help with that.

S T	Situation or Task	When I sent the draft of the new Office Supplies contract back to you for changes ...
A	Action	The problems weren't corrected by June 11 as we agreed.
R	Result	Because the corrections weren't made, the Director of Procurement had to pay overtime for two employees to do this work in order to meet our July 15 contract deadline.
A	Alternate Action	How do you think we can avoid this happening in the future? *(Solicit the employee's suggestions. Ask "What else?" several times to prompt additional ideas.)*
R	Enhanced Result	How do you think the outcome will be different?

Things to Remember when Using STAR/AR

1. Only address one issue in a conversation. If 2 or more areas need to be addressed, go back and re-define your expectations, and provide 1:1 training to close the performance gap before giving constructive feedback.

2. Manage the conversation so there is an action plan to address the performance issue or skill gap, and an action plan to solve the problem.

3. When a teammate shares his/her perspective, listen and stay on point with the intention of getting to new actions the teammate will take to change his/her behavior. Don't get sidetracked or respond to reasons why he/she didn't complete a task. Let them know you heard them and that you will discuss solutions regarding those areas later.

4. For constructive feedback, refrain from using the word "you" when addressing step 3. For example, you could say "The item was due on this date and I received it on this date" rather than directly stating "You missed a deadline."

Learning Activity #6
STAR/AR Feedback Practice

Choose one of these scenarios, or use one of your own, and write your STAR/AR feedback. Remember to include concrete, observable actions.

A. You have an employee who is unfocused and socializing more than appropriate It is starting to bother other employees. What feedback do you provide?

B. One of your employees is negative about everything. He/she is productive but upsets people by spreading rumors and complaining. What feedback do you give?

C. One of your employees is often late completing tasks. It hasn't affected results to date, but it annoys others in the department. What do you say?

D. In a performance review for an employee you know could be doing better, he/she is shocked that you question his/her performance. How do you respond?

S **T**	Situation or Task	*What was the performance challenge, opportunity or task?*
A	Action	*What did they say or do that didn't meet the standard?*
R	Result	*What was the impact of their actions on you or others?*

A	Alternate Action	*What new action should be taken to reach a more effective result?*
R	Enhanced Result	*What is likely to occur as a result of taking the alternate action?*

Conduct Effective Performance Reviews

There are some basics of performance reviews such as observation, ways to provide feedback, and goal setting.

When delivering performance reviews, remember:

Dos	Don'ts
Plan for enough time when you will not be disturbed	Don't make value judgments or comparisons
Listen, listen, listen; aim for a 50/50 discussion	Don't use words such as *always, never, best, bad, weaknesses*
Use clear and simple language during the discussion	Don't label the employee as a *poor performer*. Remember to focus on the *behavior*.
Provide support and encouragement	Don't apologize when giving constructive feedback
Use SMART goals	Don't be vague

In addition, every campus has its own process it uses. Be sure to check with your human resources to confirm you're fulfilling your campus-based responsibilities.

SMART Goals

A useful way of making goals more powerful is to use the SMART mnemonic. While there are plenty of variants (some of which we've included in parenthesis), SMART usually stands for:

- *S – Specific (or Significant)*
- *M – Measurable (or Meaningful)*
- *A – Attainable (or Action-Oriented)*
- *R – Relevant (or Rewarding)*
- *T – Time-bound (or Trackable)*

For example, instead of having "keep our department's webpage up-to-date" as a goal, it's more powerful to use the SMART goal:

"The first Friday of every month, solicit updates and new material from our department's managers for the web page; publish this new material no later than the following Friday."

Obviously, this will only be attainable if a lot of preparation has been completed beforehand!

Action Plan
Ideas for your Performance Reviews

1. What techniques will I use to observe my direct report's behavior and technical performance? How frequently will I do it?

2. Do I have individual meetings with my direct reports so we can discuss what actions are necessary to perform the work at the highest level?

3. What are the key tasks and behaviors that my direct report will be accountable for? By when will I outline these?

4. What measurements will I use to evaluate employees? Are they reasonable and justifiable measurements? Have I communicated these measurements to my employee? When will these be implemented?

5. Who else needs to be involved?

Recognize Successful Performance

What is Performance?

> ## Performance = Ability x Motivation
>
> - **Ability** is the person's talents, skills, or proficiencies in a particular area, as well as the training and resources supplied by the organization.
>
> - **Motivation** is the product of desire and commitment.

Learning Activity #7
Assessing Ability

Find a partner and discuss different ways you can determine a person's ability

Enhancing Ability

There are five main ways to overcome performance problems associated with a lack of ability. Consider using them in this sequence, which starts with the least intrusive:

1. Resupply
2. Retrain
3. Refit
4. Reassign
5. Release

Providing a Motivating Environment

One of the biggest performance challenges you will encounter is when an employee has the ability to perform the job well, directions and goals are clear, and they have all the proper resources, but their motivation is low. In these situations you should begin by helping the employee recognize and understand the negative consequences of their behavior.

A lack of motivation could be caused by a number of problems including personal, family, and financial issues. As a supervisor, you are not responsible for helping employees solve these issues but you can refer to them to resources such as your Employee Assistance Program (EAP) to get help.

In his book, "Drive: The Surprising Truth on What Motivates Us" the author Daniel Pink debunks the myth that money is motivator. In addition, he goes on to highlight research which suggests that supervisors can increase employee motivation with knowledge workers by creating an environment where they have:

- autonomy
- mastery
- purpose

Personalize Your Motivational Approach

Your team is made up of individuals who have their own unique circumstances, backgrounds, and experiences. Consequently, each person may be driven by different motivating factors, be more or less adept at self-motivation, and require a different level of autonomy, mastery, and purpose.

When you make an effort to understand each employee, you can help them stay motivated.

Learning Activity #8
Uncovering Internal Motivators

The most effective way to uncover internal motivators is to have a candid conversation with each of your team members. In this exercise, you'll prepare for that conversation by first assessing your own motivators.

1. On a scale of 1-5 (5 being the highest), assess *your* need for autonomy, mastery and purpose in the table below.

2. Now think about 1 or 2 of your employees and consider *their* motivators. Where do you think they fall on the 1-5 scale?

	Autonomy	**Mastery**	**Purpose**
You			
Employee			
Employee			

Action Plan
Are You Meeting Your Employees' Needs?

On your Action Plan, write the next steps you'll take to find out your team members' motivators and what drives their engagement. What questions will you ask to check the assessment you made in the table above?

Increase Employee Engagement

The Conference Board defines employee engagement as:

"a heightened emotional connection that an employee feels for his or her organization that influences him or her to exert greater discretionary effort to the work."

Engagement occurs when employees believe that they and the organization are supporting each other to meet their goals.

Why Engagement Matters

Put simply, employee engagement means better productivity, performance and satisfaction. Engaged employees are more likely to make extra effort, and to be invested in positive outcomes. This level of performance results in more personal satisfaction for individuals, as well as better retention, stronger loyalty and greater success for the organization.

In 2015/16, Gallup used data from more than 195,000 US organizations to analyze the relationship between employee engagement and organizational outcomes. Their study measured differences between the top 25 and the bottom 25 percent of engaged employees and found that organizations with the most engaged employees have:

- 41 percent lower absenteeism

- 59 percent lower turnover

- 70 percent fewer safety incidents

- 40 percent fewer quality issues

- 10 percent higher customer satisfaction

- 17 percent higher productivity

- 21 percent higher profitability.

The Gallup study clearly showed the benefits of employee engagement and demonstrated that engagement is a key differentiator.

"State of the American Workplace", Gallup 2016

What Leads to Engagement?

There are clear advantages in having engaged employees who are emotionally and psychologically invested in their organization's success. But how can we make that happen?

This question that has been studied by countless researchers, and while there is no magic formula, there is general agreement on the key drivers which include an employee's relationship with their direct supervisor. In other words, you!

Key Drivers of Employee Engagement		
1	**Connection of employee performance to organizational performance**	Employees understand their role in supporting the organization, and can explain their contribution to strategic goals and performance.
2	**Relationship with supervisor**	Supervisors are seen as trustworthy, reliable and supportive of their employees.
3	**Nature of the job**	Employees find satisfaction and intellectual stimulation in their work.
4	**Career growth**	Growth and development opportunities are available.
5	**Pride about the organization**	Employees are pleased and honored to be part of the organization.
6	**Relationship with co-workers**	Employees enjoy friendly, collaborative relationships with colleagues.

Learning Activity #9
Reviewing Engagement Drivers

Review the key drivers of employee engagement. List how you could influence them positively by what you do or don't do. Remember to focus on clear, actionable items.

KEY DRIVERS	DO	DON'T
Connection of employee performance to organizational performance *Employees understand their role in supporting the organization, and can explain their contribution to strategic goals and performance.*		
Relationship with supervisor *Supervisors are seen as trustworthy, reliable and supportive of their employees.*		
Nature of the job *Employees find satisfaction and intellectual stimulation in their work.*		
Career growth opportunities *Growth and development opportunities are available.*		
Pride about the organization *Employees are pleased and honored to be part of the organization.*		
Relationship with co-workers *Employees enjoy friendly, collaborative relationships with colleagues.*		

Connecting Employee Performance to Organizational Performance

An analysis of more than 300 potential drivers of engagement found that a connection between jobs and the work unit's mission and goals is the top driver of discretionary effort among employees.

The table below lists three critical types of information you can provide to employees to ensure they feel connected. Complete the 2nd row with details on where they can find this important information.

Who We Are	Why We Exist	How You Help Us Succeed
Our university's and department's goals and strategies. How we operate, and what leadership hopes to achieve.	Our university's and department's mission and vision: why our strategy and goals matter.	How your employee's role helps achieve the mission and vision to support our university's and the department's existence.
Where to find this info:	Where to find this info:	Where to find this info:

Action Plan
Increasing Employee Engagement

1. What recognition and encouragement are important to my employees?

2. How do I find out?

3. What can I do to provide the most motivating and engaging environment?

4. When will I do it by?

Module Three

Guiding and Organizing the Work

The Basic Functions of Management and Its Impact on Goal Achievement

High performance doesn't just happen. In this activity you will learn what needs to be in place for a team to effectively achieve a goal.

 Learning Activity #10
Spaghetti Tower

Build the tallest structure you can using only spaghetti and marshmallows. The structure should be stable enough to stand on its own (unsupported by anything) for one hour.

Ground rules

- Use as many marshmallows and as much spaghetti as you want
- Everyone must have a role
- Listen to each other's ideas without interrupting
- Give each other feedback along the way

Instructions

- Divide into groups
- You have 30 minutes to accomplish the goal
- When the facilitator says begin, begin!

Things to Consider

- What general approach or strategy will help you build the tallest, most stable structure?
- How much time should you spend planning? How will you plan?
- Who will do what? Use people's strengths
- Who will monitor progress or time?

The Basic Functions of Management

Every organization needs to develop and implement the basic four management functions in order to achieve its goals. These functions are:

Planning	Organizing
• Establishing strategy for achieving goals	• Determining what needs to be done
• Communicating and involving employees	• Establishing organizational/team structure
• Identifying and tapping into individual strengths	• Assigning tasks and responsibilities
• Not waiting for perfection or all the information to make decisions	• Setting schedules to meet goals
• Supporting the organization's/team's decisions/direction	• Clarifying roles
	• Communicating and delegating
	• Seeking ideas and consensus

Directing	Monitoring
• Expecting individual accountability	• Guiding the work
• Providing guidance and support	• Comparing results to goal
• Being available for questions	• Solving problems
• Communicating and motivating	• Communicating and celebrating achievements
• Inspiring action and empowering your team	• Identifying lessons learned
• Taking time to reward and recognize	• Finding ways to improve repeated processes

Learning Activity #11
Group Debrief and Self-Reflection

Group debrief

1. What lessons did you learn about goal achievement from this activity?

2. With regard to planning, did your team:

    a. Have a clear / specific strategy for achieving the goal? If not, why not?

    b. Tap into strengths (experience) of team members. If not, why not?

3. With regard to organizing, did your team assign tasks or responsibilties to different people? If not, why not?

Self-reflection

1. What lessons can you apply from this activity to your own development?

How to Delegate Work

What is Delegation?

Delegation is the assignment of tasks and responsibility from one person to another - usually from a manager to a subordinate.

Thoughtful delegation can benefit managers and employees in many ways.

Benefits For Managers	Benefits For Employees
• Demonstrates trust and willingness to invest in employee growth	• Gives employees a chance to demonstrate their potential
• Can free up manager time for more complex tasks	• Provides 'real-world' growth opportunities
• Provides cost savings by having less expensive resources complete work	• Empowers employees and expands responsibilities
• Extends capabilities and 'reach' of the team	• Increases sense of autonomy, confidence and motivation

Delegation Process

When delegating work, be sure to discuss the following key points with employees:

- **What** work or tasks you plan to delegate.
- **Why** you're delegating this work, and why you chose this employee.
- **How** the work should be completed (if applicable. With more capable employees, assign the work but not the method).
- **When** you and your employee will connect on progress.
- **How** you will support your employee to help them improve.

Learning Activity #12
Common Delegation Styles

	Advantages of using this style?	Disadvantages of using this style?	Appropriate times to use this style?
Delegate and Walk Away			
Delegate and Stay Close			
Delegate and Coach			

Tips for Success

To enable success, make sure that you:

- Assign the right person.   You need somebody who has (or can learn) the requisite skills, and who will be motivated to do the work.

- Assign the necessary level of authority.

- Provide clear expectations on schedule and results.

- Solicit the employee's ideas and input.

- Offer support if needed.

- Reward results.

Supervising in a Unionized Environment

Learning Activity #13
Collective Bargaining Agreement Scenarios

In small groups read each scenario and then answer the discussion questions:

Situation A

One of your direct reports is in the bargaining unit represented by the California State University Employees Union (Unit 7 – Clerical/Administrative Support Services). She is classified as an ASC1. She informs you that the work she is performing more properly should be classified as an AA/S, which is a higher classification.

What should you do?

- Review the labor contract with the employee
- Contact the union labor representative on campus
- Reach out to HR/Labor Relations
- Approve a Request for Position Classification Review

Situation B

You are the Chair of the Physics Department. It has recently come to your attention that one of the faculty members in your department has been accused by a graduate student of sexual harassment.

What should you do?

- Review the labor contract with the employee
- Contact the union representative on campus
- Reach out to HR/Labor Relations / your Title IX Coordinator
- Have a conversation with the faculty member about sexual harassment

Situation C

You are the Administrator of Fleet Services. Your department maintains vehicles and ensures that staff and faculty operate the University's fleet safely. After analyzing the work hours of all three automotive mechanics, you have decided to change their work hours to improve efficiency. The mechanics are in the bargaining unit represented by the Teamsters (Unit 6 – Skilled Trades) and have said that you don't have the right to set work hours.

What should you do?

- Review the labor contract with the employees
- Contact the union representative on campus
- Reach out to HR/labor Relations
- Change the hours as planned

Whom to Contact When You Have Labor Relations Questions

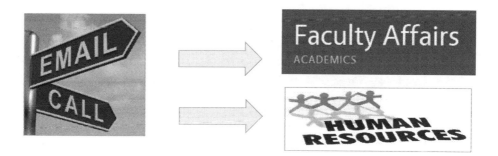

If you are supervising labor-represented employees for the first time, make sure to seek guidance from the Labor and Employee Relations experts on your campus. Check the CSU Labor and Employee Relations site for more information: https://www2.calstate.edu/csu-system/faculty-staff/labor-and-employee-relations/

Any questions regarding the supervision of unionized staff should be directed to your Human Resources Department. Questions regarding the supervision of unionized faculty should be directed to Faculty Affairs.

How Higher Education Differs from Private Sector

Scott Cowen, president of Tulane University, summed up the challenges of leadership in business schools. In his remarks at the 1996 outgoing president of AACSB—The International Association for Management Education. He posed the question, "Are we operating our schools in a way that promotes high quality, continuous improvement and assurance to those we serve that we practice what we preach?" then answered his own question in the following way:

"Assume that you were told the following characteristics of a hypothetical organization in a hypothetical industry:

1. The services provided are driven by what the organization wants to do.

2. Customer service/responsiveness is anathema to the organization's culture.

3. A majority of the organization's costs are fixed and committed.

4. A significant percentage of its workforce has lifetime employment contracts, without incentive compensation or a systematic performance review process.

5. The culture often values process more than results.

6. The organization's key human resource can spend at least 20% of its time on activities external to the organization, including working for a competitor.

7. The leaders of the organization often lack the knowledge and skills needed to lead and manage an effective organization.

To the extent that the management schools or institutions of higher education share any of the characteristics of our hypothetical organization, we cannot answer this question in the affirmative. As we all know, our institutions are not built for speed, rapid change or just-in-time operations. This is our beauty as well as our bane... Last fall, I heard the former president of an outstanding university comment that, 'If the Edsel were an academic department, it would still be in existence.'

The Culture of Higher Education

Organizations try to encourage consistent, observable patterns of behavior, common structures, consistent messages and coherent goals to build effective cultures. This can be challenging in universities where academics often see the institutional requirements as being less important than the demands of their professional or disciplinary affiliations. These allegiances can sometimes work against the broader goals of your university.

Aspects of Culture

To successfully supervise in higher education, it is important to understand the influences that are likely to impact your work. As you review the different aspects of academic culture below, think about how evident they are in your university.

Collaboration	High demands of committees, meetings, collegial expectations, and institutional 'red tape'
Collegiality	Colleagues positively interact, respect each other, and value the contributions of each individual
Critical thinking	Faculty like to make inferences about the object of study, abstracting patterns, meaning, and significance from data, and then subjecting those inferences to rigorous testing
Commitment to scholarship and research	Research and scholarship are valued and supported; mentors and other sources of career guidance are available
Commitment to student development	Staff are actively committed to providing high-quality learning experiences and monitoring student well-being
Commitment to teaching and learning	Teaching and professional staff focus on quality teaching and learning processes and outcomes
Job satisfaction	High level of satisfaction with working in the university – may be influenced by workloads, remuneration, sense of autonomy, opportunity
Multicultural orientation	High diversity in the student population
Advocacy	Emphasizes addressing inequity and imbalance
Developmental	Encourages high level of professional development and growth

Types of Culture

The overall culture of your university and its constituent sub-groups (faculty, staff, students, etc.) depends on the values, ideologies and messages conveyed.

What are the dominant values that are influencing your university? Consider the following cultural descriptions, which have been divided according to three broad types of organizational culture: collegial, bureaucratic and political. Evaluate each cultural description, assessing the degree to which it matches your university culture.

Collegial

- Ideas and perspectives are sought when a new issue emerges
- Mistakes are seen as learning opportunities
- Junior and senior colleagues talk freely about issues. If a problem is identified, members feel comfortable in raising an issue for discussion
- The community celebrates the achievement of its members
- Knowledge within the community can be accessed by others at point of need
- There are regular opportunities to hear about what is happening

Bureaucratic

- If things go wrong, someone has to take the blame
- Innovation is seen as risky and not encouraged
- Junior staff are not included in decision-making or reviews of strategy
- Permissions have to be sought to take actions
- The organizational structures are clearly outlined and followed
- There are strong policies and rules that we need to adhere to

Political

- It is important to have a sponsor to ensure you get considered for opportunities
- It is not what you know, but who you know
- Knowledge of institutional activities, directions is withheld by those in power
- Resources are allocated on perceived value, not a predictable formula
- There is a hierarchy of status that drives who is included and who is not
- When things go wrong, a scapegoat will be sought

Manage Your Time

There will always be competing priorities. There will always be other projects waiting to derail your day. There will always be changes and last-minute requests. You can't stop that but you can be more efficient with your time.

How to Stay Focused on the Important Stuff

To help you get to the "desired" state and focus on priorities, use these time management tips:

- Have daily and weekly plans that address your goals and everything that you need to accomplish in that time

- Complete your most important tasks first

- Match your energy level to the importance of your task

- Use different features of Microsoft Outlook (Task List, Calendar, Contacts List, etc.).

- Organize your office and your desk so that you can find things

- Avoid procrastination

- Learn to be assertive, projecting self-confidence without coming across as arrogant

- Identify and eliminate time-wasting activities

- Practice scheduling time buffers on your electronic calendar

- Focus and block out distractions

- Create a "stop doing" list

Use the Urgent-Important Matrix to Be More Productive

The Urgent-Important Matrix (also called the Eisenhower Matrix) is used to visually identify the most effective use of time.

	Urgent	Not Urgent
Important	**Quadrant A** Important and urgent items are things you should do *now*, such as critical tasks with a firm deadline.	**Quadrant B** Important but not urgent work includes tasks that are valuable and productive, but which can be scheduled. For example, coaching employees.
Not Important	**Quadrant C** Not important but urgent items include work that *feels* imperative but which could actually be postponed or delegated without negative consequences. For example, responding immediately to texts and email.	**Quadrant D** Not important and not urgent tasks are ones you could – and probably should – eliminate, such as sorting through junk mail or frequently checking social media.

**Learning Activity #14
Urgent-Important Matrix Assessment**

In the following activity, you'll assess your current time management habits then plot your results to evaluate whether you're effectively using your time.

1. Circle your responses to each to the eight questions below.

QUESTIONS	Strongly Disagree	Disagree	Slightly Disagree	Slightly Agree	Agree	Strongly Agree
1. I spend much of my time on important activities that demand my immediate attention such as crises, pressing problems, and deadline-driven projects.	1	2	3	4	5	6
2. I feel I am always "putting out fires" and working in a crisis mode.	1	2	3	4	5	6
3. I feel I waste a lot of time.	1	2	3	4	5	6
4. I spend much of my time on activities that have little relevance to my top priorities, but demand my immediate attention (e.g., needless interruptions, unimportant meetings, non-critical calls and email).	1	2	3	4	5	6
5. I spend much of my time on activities that are important but not urgent, such as planning, preparation, prevention relationship building, and self-renewal.	1	2	3	4	5	6
6. I spend much of my time on busywork, compulsive habits, junk mail, excessive TV, texting, blogging, etc.	1	2	3	4	5	6
7. I feel I am on top of things because of careful preparation, planning, and prevention	1	2	3	4	5	6
8. I feel I am constantly addressing issues that are important to others, but not to me.	1	2	3	4	5	6

2. Add your scores for the following questions.

Quadrant A		Quadrant B		Quadrant C		Quadrant D	
Q1	___	Q5	___	Q4	___	Q3	___
Q2	___	Q7	___	Q8	___	Q6	___
Total	___	Total	___	Total	___	Total	___

3. Color each segment below to correspond with the quadrant totals above. What do you notice?   Do you need to make any changes?

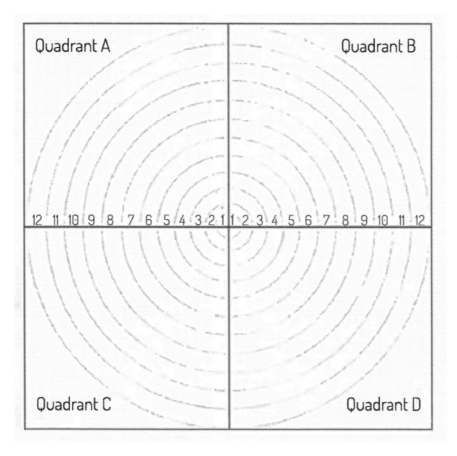

Used with permission of franklincovey.com

**Action Plan
Delegation**

1. Which job tasks could be delegated to others? Why? Is there someone on my staff who could do the work? What are the risk factors?

2. When will I delegate the tasks?

3. What will I do to move tasks from quadrant to quadrant to make optimum use of my time?

Module Four

Managing Relationships

How Trustworthy Do You Think You Are?

Becoming trustworthy in relationships begins with examining your own behaviors in the four domains of trust: Able, Believable, Connected, and Dependable.

Learning Activity #15
How Trustworthy Do You Think You Are?

Using the response legend to the right, complete the following self-assessment to discover your strengths as well as the areas where you can improve. Circle your responses.

Response Legend:
Hardly Ever
Sometimes
Often
Very Often
Always

A – Able

When you demonstrate competence and skills, you are ABLE, which builds trust.

Below are some statements about your **ability**. Think about your behaviors in a specific work role, e.g., manager or individual contributor. In this role, how often do you behave in each of the listed ways? Choose one response that best describes your behavior.

1. Get quality results	H	S	O	V	A
2. Solve problems	H	S	O	V	A
3. Am highly skilled	H	S	O	V	A
4. Am good at what I do	H	S	O	V	A
5. Have relevant experience	H	S	O	V	A
6. Use my skills to assist others	H	S	O	V	A
7. Strive to be the best at what I do	H	S	O	V	A

Subtotal

B – Believable

When you act with integrity, you are BELIEVABLE, which builds trust.

Below are some statements about your **believability.** Thinking about the same role you choose to analyze for the ABLE area of trust, how often do you behave in each of the listed ways? Choose one response that best describes your behavior.

	H S O V A
8. Keep confidences	H S O V A
9. Admit when I am wrong	H S O V A
10. Am honest	H S O V A
11. Avoid talking behind people's backs	H S O V A
12. Am sincere	H S O V A
13. Am non-judgmental	H S O V A
14. Show respect for others	H S O V A
Subtotal	

C – Connected

When you care about others, you are CONNECTED, which builds trust.

Below are some statements about your **connectedness.** Thinking about the same role you chose to analyze for the ABLE and BELIEVABLE areas of trust, how often do you behave in each of the listed ways? Choose one response that best describes your behavior.

	H S O V A
15. Listen well	H S O V A
16. Praise others' efforts	H S O V A
17. Show interest in others	H S O V A
18. Share about myself	H S O V A
19. Work well with others	H S O V A
20. Show empathy for others	H S O V A
21. Ask for input	H S O V A
Subtotal	

D – Dependable
When you maintain reliability, you are DEPENDABLE, which builds trust.

Below are some statements about your dependability. Thinking about the same role you chose to analyze for the ABLE, BELIEVABLE, and CONNECTED areas of trust, how often do you behave in each of the listed ways? Choose one response that best describes your behavior.

	H	S	O	V	A
22. Do what I say I will do	H	S	O	V	A
23. Am timely	H	S	O	V	A
24. Am responsive to requests	H	S	O	V	A
25. Am organized	H	S	O	V	A
26. Am accountable for my actions	H	S	O	V	A
27. Follow up	H	S	O	V	A
28. Am consistent	H	S	O	V	A
Subtotal					

Scoring

Transfer the subtotals of the number of circles in each column and note below. Multiply by each factor for your total score.

	A	B	C	D	x	Factor	=	A	B	C	D
H					x	1	=				
S					x	2	=				
O					x	3	=				
V					x	4	=				
A					x	5	=				
Total											

The scoring legend shows your strength in each area of the ABCD Trust Model™.

33 – 35	Outstanding! You've mastered this area.
30 – 32	Good. You're on the right track.
27 – 29	Average. Keep working at it.
Below 27	Pay attention! Lots of room for improvement here.

Take a few minutes to reflect on the following:

1. Who is someone you completely trust? Why?

2. In which work relationships do I want to develop a deep level of trust? Why?

3. How do I develop that deep level of trust in others?

4. How can I inspire others to develop that level of trust in me?

Communication Challenges

Learning Activity #16
Potential Communication Problems

Listen to parts 1 & 2 of the phone conversation role play then discuss these questions at your table:

a. Did your perception of this conversation change between part 1 and 2?
b. Have you ever been involved in a situation where you or someone else did not have all the information? What problems did this cause?

Now examine the graph below and discuss the following questions:

a. How do you interpret this graph?
b. How is this feedback data related to the phone conversation you heard?
c. Think back to before you were a supervisor. Does this data seem accurate?
d. This data covers feedback on areas where employees need to improve, and how to maximize their strengths. What other situations did you feel you did not have enough communication?
e. What implications does this have for you as a supervisor?

Feedback: Manager versus Employee Perceptions

| Employees receive sufficient feedback or advice on areas in which they need improvement. | Managers Agree 89% |
| | Employees Agree 57% |

| Employees receive sufficient feedback or advice on how to maximize their strengths. | Managers Agree 89% |
| | Employees Agree 49% |

Survey data used with permission of Development Dimensions International (DDI).

"The day soldiers stop bringing you their problems is the day you have stopped leading them." General Colin Powell

Essential Communication Skills

Learning Activity #17
Sharing Your Knowledge on Essential Communication

You already know a lot about communication and what will be important to remember as a supervisor. In your small group, list recommendations for your assigned communication topic. Then capture your group's insights on the appropriate flipchart in the room.

Clear Verbal Communication

Active Listening

Facilitating Effective Meetings

Sharing Your Knowledge on Essential Communication Skills

Clear Verbal Communication

- Have an open mind and suspend your ego
- Be specific
- Ask clarifying questions
- Make good eye contact
- Remove all distractions and focus on the individual
- Think before you speak
- Avoid interruptions and judgments
- Tailor the message in mood, energy, language, and body language
- Tell stories
- Shut up and listen!

Active Listening

Dos	Don'ts
• Be attentive, interested, curious	• Interrupt
• Listen for tone and inflection	• Contradict
• Nod and respond approvingly	• Complete speakers sentences
• Acknowledge speaker's feelings	• Show impatience
• Allow speaker time to find words	• Be judgmental
• Ask clarifying questions	• Make assumptions
• Paraphrase and summarize	

Non-verbal Communication

Experts believe that a significant proportion of communication is non-verbal.

Albert Mehrabian, Professor of Psychology at UCLA, found that more than 50% of messages around feelings and attitudes are conveyed via non-verbal communication. It's important to keep this in mind when discussing sensitive topics with employees, such as poor performance or workplace changes which could provoke an emotional but non-verbal response.

Foster Teamwork

The Benefits of Teamwork

- Teams accomplish tasks faster and more efficiently than individuals.

- Cooperating together on various tasks reduces workloads for all employees by enabling them to share responsibilities or ideas.

- Teams reduce the work pressure on every worker, which allows them to be thorough in the completion of the assigned roles.

- Teamwork increases accountability because team members do not want to let each other down.

- Teams typically have members with different skill levels. Working together helps employees improve skills and acquire new ones.

Do You Supervise a Team or a Group of Individuals?

Jon R. Katzenback and Douglas K. Smith, authors of the Harvard Business Review article "The Discipline of Teams", define a team as "a small number of people with complementary skills who are committed to a common purpose, performance goals, and approach for which they hold themselves mutually accountable."

Having clarity regarding the identity of your direct reports as a team or a group can facilitate work getting done faster and at a higher level of quality.

Investing time upfront to discuss a group's goals, roles and purpose will help clarify if it should function as a real team or as a group of individuals.

Confusion about these core group elements can be the root cause of mediocre engagement and stifled productivity.

Groups		Teams
Individual accountability	or	Individual and mutual accountability
Come together to share information and perspectives	or	Frequently come together for discussion, decisions making, problem solving, and planning
Focus on individual goals	or	Focus on team goals
Produce individual work products	or	Produce collective work products
Define individual roles, responsibilities, and tasks	or	Define individual roles, responsibilities, and tasks to help team do its work; often share and rotate them
Mainly concerned with one's own outcome and challenges	or	Concerned with outcomes of everyone and challenges the team faces
Purpose, goals, approach to work shaped by supervisor	or	Purpose, goals, approach to work shaped by supervisor and team members

Learning Activity #18
Team Effectiveness Questionnaire

Answer these questions for the team you currently supervise.

		Strongly Disagree	Disagree	Neutral	Agree	Strongly Agree
1.	The mission and goals of this team are clear to all members.	1	2	3	4	5
2.	Each member of team is clear on his or her roles and responsibilities.	1	2	3	4	5
3.	Communication in our team is open and honest.	1	2	3	4	5
4.	The team has well established and agreed upon approaches to decision-making and problem solving.	1	2	3	4	5
5.	There are ground rules/norms in place to guide team functioning.	1	2	3	4	5
6.	Each team member understands what involved and effective team participation looks like.	1	2	3	4	5
7.	Team members help one another deal with problems or resolve issues.	1	2	3	4	5
8.	Our team has a meaningful, shared mission.	1	2	3	4	5
9.	Team members understand one another's roles and responsibilities.	1	2	3	4	5
10.	Team members listen effectively to one another.	1	2	3	4	5
11.	Team problem-solving results in effective solutions.	1	2	3	4	5
12.	Ground rules/norms are clearly understood by all team members.	1	2	3	4	5
13.	Team members avoid duplication of effort and make sure they are clear about who is doing what.	1	2	3	4	5
14.	The team tries to address problems before they become larger.	1	2	3	4	5
15.	When goals are set for the team they are specific and measurable.	1	2	3	4	5
16.	Each team member has been given an updated job description.	1	2	3	4	5
17.	Supervisors model communication skills they expect from team members.	1	2	3	4	5

18.	As appropriate, team members use consensus to decide important issues.	1	2	3	4	5
19.	Team members have the opportunity to give input on ground rules/norms.	1	2	3	4	5
20.	Team members show high levels of cooperation and mutual support.	1	2	3	4	5
21.	The team periodically evaluates its functioning and processes.	1	2	3	4	5
22.	Each member of the team understands how his or her job connects to the mission of our work unit or department.	1	2	3	4	5
23.	Team members routinely update each other on their projects/work.	1	2	3	4	5
24.	Team members routinely provide constructive feedback to each other.	1	2	3	4	5
25.	Team members understand different decision-making methods.	1	2	3	4	5
26.	The team frequently revisits ground rules/norms.	1	2	3	4	5
27.	Different methods are used to help introverts contribute or share info.	1	2	3	4	5
28.	After completing large projects team members discuss lessons learned.	1	2	3	4	5
	Column Score This is the sum of the numbers in each column. E.g., if you circled "5" (Strongly Agree) 4 times, then your score for that column is 20.					
	Total Score This is the sum of all columns.					

Team Effectiveness Questionnaire Scoring

Part 1: Total Score Interpretation

Score	Comment
28-65	This isn't good, but look on the bright side; you have a lot of opportunities to help your team be more effective.
66-102	Your team probably isn't as effective as it could be. It does some things well, but there's room for improvement. Determine where to start by analyzing your component scores in Part 2 (below).
103-140	Congratulations! Your team is effective.

Part 2: Component Score Results

Clear Mission and Team Goals		Clearly-Defined Roles		Clear Communication		Well-Balanced Decision-Making Procedures	
Question #	Score	Question #	Score	Question #	Score	Question #	Score
1		2		3		4	
8		9		10		11	
15		16		17		18	
22		23		24		25	
Total		Total		Total		Total	
Average (total ÷ 4)		Average (total ÷ 4)		Average (total ÷ 4)		Average (total ÷ 4)	

Established Ground Rules		Balanced Participation		Improvement Plans	
Question #	Score	Question #	Score	Question #	Score
5		6		7	
12		13		14	
19		20		21	
26		27		28	
Total		Total		Total	
Average (total ÷ 4)		Average (total ÷ 4)		Average (total ÷ 4)	

Instructions

- Share your total score with a partner
- Discuss:
    - What do your component score results tell you?
    - Are there any surprises?
    - Which of the components do you need to improve most?

Characteristics of High-Performing Teams

There are seven components which distinguish high-performing teams from those that experience problems.

Component	Definition	Potential Issue If Missing	Actions to Take
1. Clear Mission and Team Goals CLARITY	Teams often assume their goals are clear and then later experience mistakes due to confusion. Goals need to be specific, attainable, and well-communicated.	When team goals are not clear, potential troubles may include frequent disagreement about next steps, frustration at the lack of progress and excessive questioning of group decisions and actions.	A. Have a mission. B. Explain how each employee's job connects to mission (purpose). C. Set S.M.A.R.T. Goals.
2. Clearly Defined Roles ROLE	To clearly define roles of a team, you need to design formal roles and responsibilities, set clear boundaries for each role, and design job/ team responsibilities that use each member's talents, and rotate general roles.	When there are no clearly defined roles, the skills of team members will not be fully utilized. There may be confusion over which team member has a specific task, and some may get more than their share of tedious chores.	A. Have up-to-date job descriptions for each employee (get employees to help). B. Ask employees to update you and each other on projects/work they are doing.
3. Clear Communication	Clear communication exists when team members speak with clarity and directness, listen actively, explore ideas rather than argue over them, openly share information, and provide constructive feedback rather than criticism.	Teams with poor communication have members who have a tendency to withhold information, discount others' ideas, and opinions, and cover up true feelings.	A. Role model good communication (listening) skills. B. Don't use email for first communication of important information. C. Set clear expectations about giving feedback.

Component	Definition	Potential Issue If Missing	Actions to Take
4. Well-Defined Decision Procedures	When teams develop effective decision-making procedures they explore important issues by polling members, decide important issues by consensus, use high-quality data as a basis for decisions, and agree who will make what decision.	Without well-defined decision-making procedures, teams find it difficult to break out of the old orientation of being told what to do as opposed to deciding for themselves.	A. Explain your role in the decision-making process. B. Set expectations how decisions will be made. C. Train employees on decision-making methods.
5. Established Ground Rules/ Norms	Establishing rules for the team involves the process of members deciding what are acceptable and unacceptable behaviors within the team for both tasks and relationships.	Without openly stated rules, teams experience frustration and confusion with other members' behaviors. Potential troubles may include members who continue behavior that frustrates other team members.	A. Involve employees in process of establishing team ground rules/norms. B. Revisit norms ground rules/norms on regular basis.
6. Balanced Participation	This strategy not only contributes to getting the job done, but it develops all members' expertise in all areas, which strengthens the team's performance.	Without balanced participation, performance can result in certain members having too much or too little influence based on their skill set, and cross-job coverage not supporting productivity goals.	A. Set expectation that employees need to be involved. Explain what involvement looks like. B. Use different methods to keep employees engaged in meetings.

7. **Improvement Plans** 	The goal of an improvement plan is to ensure high team performance. The plan needs to cover five activities: • Maintain communications • Fix obvious problems • Look upstream to larger issues • Document progress and problems • Monitor changes	Without an improvement plan, the team may use ineffective approaches to address problems that result in little or no improvement of team output.	A. Routinely assess team performance after projects. B. Keep track of lessons learned.

Overcoming Common Problems in Teams

When a team is experiencing problems such as competing loyalties or failing to meet performance expectations, each team member is responsible for trying to ensure that everyone gets along. Some problems, however, require a more structured approach.

The following outlines typical team problems:

Floundering	The team is either unclear about its tasks or overwhelmed by them. This usually occurs in the early stages of team development. Planning is essential to minimize floundering.
Dominating Participant	A team member who talks a lot, consuming the team's time. He/she may or may not have specific expertise, but tends to tell long stories or give unnecessary detail.

Silent Participant	A team member who rarely speaks and if asked about his/her silence, may say, "I'm listening, when I have something to say, I'll say it." Team performance can suffer when a silent participant does not speak up when it would be beneficial. Some people, based on their individual preferences have different comfort levels speaking in a group (e.g., extroverts versus introverts).
Digression and Tangents	One team member describes a past situation relevant to the problem at hand. This triggers the memory of other team members who begin describing similar situations at length. When the meeting is over, team members wonder where the time went because little was accomplished.
Rush to Accomplishment	"Doing something is better than doing nothing." This belief may cause team members be impatient or rush through a project in order to reach a conclusion when haste is inappropriate for the situation.
Discounting	One team member fails to give credit to another's ideas or ignores another person's contributions. A team member may begin to ridicule other team member's ideas or behavior. This can cause hostility and hurt feelings leading to unnecessary conflict.
Acceptance of Opinion as Fact	A team member makes statements with such confidence that other team members are reluctant to question the validity of the statement even when it is clearly an opinion rather than factual data.
Feuding Team Members	You may need to act as a mediator when this occurs. Unresolved conflict, over time, will reduce the team's overall performance.

Preventing the Blame Game

The blame game consists of blaming another person for an event or state of affairs thought to be undesirable, and persisting in it instead of proactively making changes that help the situation.

Why It Occurs

At work, the main reason employees engage in the blame game is because they don't have clear goals and responsibilities. When things aren't clear, errors are more likely to occur and employees get rattled and flustered with each other. In such a state, one's mind goes into over-drive trying to come up with a logical explanation. Neuroscience research has found that at a subconscious level we want to preserve our self-image and self-esteem. So, we look for the nearest scapegoat to pile responsibility on, washing ourselves clean of any responsibility. We engage in the blame game as a defensive mechanism.

Complaining and blaming go hand-in-hand. When we are unhappy or dissatisfied with someone or something, our feelings of negativity lead us to complain so we can relieve the inner tension we feel. Complaining is also a learned behavior. As babies we cry because we don't feel good or are hungry. Crying leads to someone fixing our problems. Many scientists believe that as adults we complain because subconsciously we want others to fix our problems. Be wary of employees who come to you, always looking for help solving problems. These employees won't learn important skills by becoming dependent on you.

What the Blame Game Looks Like

Learning Activity #19
How to Stop the Blame Game in its Tracks

To determine how susceptible your team is to the blame game, and what actions you can take to prevent it, answer each of the questions below. Put a check mark in the appropriate column.

I do this regularly	I could be better	Supervisor Actions
		I make sure each employee on my team knows their key responsibilities and performance standards.
		I lead by example. I take ownership of my mistakes and freely admit when I have made them.
		I've created an environment where employees on my team take ownership of their mistakes.
		I quickly address employees who blame or complain too frequently. If unchecked, this behavior is contagious and may spread to others on my team.
		I keep employees on my team focused on coming up with solutions, rather than problems.
		I discourage gossip on my team, for example, individuals trying to boost their own self-identity by saying something negative about another person.
		I aim to boost employees' self-esteem by providing positive feedback, highlighting strengths, rewarding good work, and asking them to share opinions and ideas.

Action Plan
Ideas for your Action Plan

1. What steps will I take to ensure I have the appropriate relationships in place?

2. How will I nurture those relationships?

3. What are my stakeholders' preferred methods of communication?

4. What do my direct reports need to work effectively together? Whose assistance will I need to get those resources? By when?

Module Five

Managing Yourself

The HEXACO-PI-R Model of Personality

Background

The **HEXACO** model of personality structure is a six-dimensional model of human personality that was created by Canadian researchers Michael Ashton and Kibeom Lee in the early 2000s.

The HEXACO-PI-R assesses the six broad HEXACO personality factors, each of which contains four "facets", or narrower personality characteristics. (An additional 25th narrow facet, called Altruism, is also included and represents a blend of the Honesty-Humility, Emotionality, and Agreeableness factors.)

The four facets within each factor are as follows:

- **Honesty-Humility (H):** Sincerity, Fairness, Greed Avoidance, Modesty

- **Emotionality (E):** Fearfulness, Anxiety, Dependence, Sentimentality

- **Extraversion (X):** Social Self-Esteem, Social Boldness, Sociability, Liveliness

- **Agreeableness (A):** Forgivingness, Gentleness, Flexibility, Patience

- **Conscientiousness (C):** Organization, Diligence, Perfectionism, Prudence

- **Openness to Experience (O):** Aesthetic Appreciation, Inquisitiveness, Creativity, Unconventionality

Learning Activity #20
Interpreting Your HEXACO-PI-R Results

Your HEXACO-PI-R Results

Shown below are your scores on the six broad "factor" scales and the 25 narrow "facet" scales of the HEXACO-PI-R. (Each factor scale is listed in bold, with its four facet scales indented below it. An additional facet scale, Altruism, is related to several factors and is listed separately.)

	Your Score	Median Score (50th percentile) *	Middle 80% of Scores (10th to 90th percentiles) *
Honesty-Humility		3.22	2.41 - 3.97
Sincerity		3.25	2.13 - 4.25
Fairness		3.38	2.13 - 4.63
Greed-Avoidance		2.63	1.38 - 4.00
Modesty		3.63	2.50 - 4.50
Emotionality		3.34	2.63 - 3.97
Fearfulness		3.00	1.88 - 4.00
Anxiety		3.75	2.63 - 4.63
Dependence		3.25	2.00 - 4.25
Sentimentality		3.50	2.38 - 4.38
eXtraversion		3.50	2.72 - 4.22
Social Self-Esteem		4.00	3.00 - 4.63
Social Boldness		3.13	1.88 - 4.25
Sociability		3.63	2.50 - 4.50
Liveliness		3.63	2.50 - 4.50
Agreeableness		3.00	2.22 - 3.72
Forgivingness		2.75	1.75 - 3.88
Gentleness		3.25	2.25 - 4.13
Flexibility		2.75	1.75 - 3.75
Patience		3.25	2.00 - 4.38
Conscientiousness		3.47	2.72 - 4.16
Organization		3.38	2.13 - 4.38
Diligence		3.88	2.88 - 4.71
Perfectionism		3.63	2.38 - 4.38
Prudence		3.25	2.13 - 4.00
Openness to Experience		3.31	2.50 - 4.13
Aesthetic Appreciation		3.25	2.00 - 4.38
Inquisitiveness		3.13	1.88 - 4.38
Creativity		3.63	2.25 - 4.63
Unconventionality		3.38	2.63 - 4.25
Altruism		3.88	3.00 - 4.63

What do the "percentile" numbers mean?

The percentiles indicate the percentage of respondents whose scores are below a given number. So, 10% of respondents are below the 10th percentile, 50% of respondents are below the 50th percentile, and 90% of respondents are below the 90th percentile.

The 50th percentile (or "median") represents the typical or average respondent.

What should I conclude from my results?

Your profile of results is meant to give you some insight into your basic personality dispositions. But you shouldn't over-interpret your results or treat them as a kind of "prophecy" for your future.

If you're disappointed with your score for a certain trait, you can still try to change some of your attitudes and behaviors related to that trait, and you can still find ways to make your level of this trait less of a problem for you (or for others).

Why are some traits given in bold, and why are others indented?

The traits given in bold are the six broad HEXACO personality factors.

The four indented traits below each of these six are the narrower "facet" level traits that belong to each factor.

The remaining trait, Altruism, is a facet that is related to three of the broad factors (Honesty-Humility, Emotionality, and Agreeableness).

Reflection Questions

1. What was your highest scoring trait?

2. How does this trait impact your ability to supervise?

3. Which of your traits scores disappointed you?

4. What can you do to make it less of a problem for you (or for others)?

Taking Accountability for Your Own Development

 Learning Activity #21
Developing Yourself

Read the Marshall Goldsmith quote then discuss the following questions with others at your table.

1. What is the key point being made?

2. How can you communicate to employees that you're developing too?

 **Action Plan**
Ideas for your Action Plan

1. Now that I know a little bit more about myself, how will I maximize or minimize my traits to enhance my work environment?

2. What should I do to take full accountability for my development?

Tips and Toolkit

Principles of SUPERVISION

Tips to Help Establish Yourself as a Supervisor

Have a Entry Strategy

If you are a first time supervisor you are entering a period in your professional and personal development unlike any other in your career. Your first year will likely be vexing as well as energizing. You will certainly be challenged. How you enter an organization or a new work unit is critical to your success.

Some people move into supervision with the grace and coordination of an Olympic gold medal skater. Most, however, experience their first year as tap dancing on marbles. There is a lot happening and a lot of energy being expended, but very little is graceful or stable or certain. The purpose of information on the following pages is to provide surer footing. Taking these steps will help you survive and thrive in your first year as a supervisor.

Step #1: Discuss Expectations and Preferences With Your Boss

Creating and maintaining a good rapport with your boss is essential to your success as a supervisor. This can be accomplished through have a clear set of expectations relating to performance and communication as well as understanding your boss' management style. Discuss these questions with your boss:

Performance Expectations

- What performance is my boss expecting of me?
- What kinds of behaviors should I avoid?
- What are my first priorities?

Communication

- What's my style and preferences for keeping others informed (when, how much, verbal, written, formal, informal, etc.)
- What are my boss's communication preferences?
- What are my boss's preferences for one-on-one meetings? (timing, frequency, etc.)
- How I prefer to get feedback?
- What are my boss's feedback preferences?

Management Style

- What is my preferred management style?
- What is my boss's preferred management style?
- What are my boss's strengths, and how can I best learn from them?
- What decisions does my boss want input on?

Personal Information

Sharing personal information can be key to building trust as well as understanding what motivates someone.

Answer these questions and decide what information you will share with your boss.

- How much of who I am (family, interests, personal goals, etc.) do I want to share with my boss?
- What are my development opportunities?

Step #2: Learn Key Information About Your University and Work Unit

In order to consistently make decisions that positively impact your university, you will need to first "know" key information. The sooner you become knowledgeable about key information, the sooner you will gain confidence and obtain the credibility of your team.

- Read your university's, work unit's, and team's mission and vision statements and strategic goals. Talk to your boss to learn how your team's mission, goals, and objectives fit into the big picture.

- Meet with each of your employees to get their thoughts about your team. Some questions to ask include:
    - What have been the major accomplishments of our team?
    - What are the challenges our team faces?
    - What is this team's mission statement? What are this year's goals and objectives?
    - What are this team's current priorities? What will they be in a month from now? Three months? Six months?

      o   Looking at the team's objectives, what are one or two things we can do to improve our performance?

      o   As a supervisor, what can I do to improve this team's performance?

      o   Which team members are experts on certain processes?

      o   Are there people on other teams we regularly work with? Who are they?

- Talk with your peers about the culture and morale of your work unit and team. Get their input on what is working, what is not working, and suggestions for improvement.

- Meet with your predecessor, if that is possible. Use this information wisely; digest it, but come to your own conclusions.

- Don't be afraid to ask questions about your daily tasks and admit you don't know something. Strong people ask basic questions; they ask for help. Strong people even ask questions when they think they know the answers.

- Do some hands-on work with your team. It will give you direct experience with the business processes in use, but it will also show the team you are willing to work hard and you care about what they do.

- Read current news articles about your industry/work function. Subscribe to Internet blogs or periodicals.

Step #3: Get to Know Your Employees

You will accomplish more in the long run by building relationships before you focus on tasks.

- Hold a team meeting and share your background and work related interests.
    - Ask each employee to do the same.
    - Use team building exercises to get to know each other better.

- Spend time with each employee getting to know them professionally.

- Show genuine concern and consideration for others - even small things, like saying please and thank you, go a long way toward building strong relationships.

- Be willing to work as hard as you expect your employees to work. Symbolically you are communicating that you value them and the work they do.

- Be accessible to your employees either in regular update meetings or more informally.

- If you are following an ineffective supervisor do not bad mouth them. Employees do not want to hear you discuss a peer in an unprofessional manner

- If you replace a respected supervisor, you might have a hard time being accepted. Openly appreciating and valuing their contributions shows others that you are confident and ready to move the area forward.

- Don't immediately start making changes. Employees don't like new people coming in and telling them what to do

Step #4: Take These Actions if You Are Managing Peers

If you have been promoted from within the same team and are supervising former peers, extra sensitivity is required on your part.

- Meet with them one-on-one and acknowledge any feelings of awkwardness.
    - Commit to utilizing their expertise and helping with their goals.
    - Discuss ways that your relationship may need to change.
- Be humble. A promotion isn't a license to be cocky.
    - You have yet to prove you are worthy of the promotion. Concentrate on that.
    - You're not a real supervisor until you perform and produce like one.
- Resist temptation to begin meddling or intervening before you officially take over. You'll have plenty of time to make your mark soon enough.
- Don't change your personality to fit some perceived stereotype of what a good supervisor is supposed to be.
- Don't forget where you came from or how you got to your *new* position.
- Respect old loyalties and friendships. It helps keep you grounded.
- Don't expect favors and don't ask for a lot of extra perks (e.g., *new* office furniture, redecorating). Remember, you're just the *new* boss, not a conquering hero.
- Don't think you have all the answers. You don't even know all the questions yet.

Step #5 : Share Information

In an environment of constant change, sharing information is critical. The more information you can share with your employees, the more valued, committed and empowered they will feel.

- Share information face-to-face, especially if it is difficult to deliver or will affect your employees in significant ways. Research shows that people react more favorably when the news is delivered in this manner.

- Beware of critical information flowing down through many layers. If it must flow down, double-check to be sure the message is getting through.

- Get creative. The more creatively a message is sent, the greater the chance it will be noticed.

    o For important messages, consider doing the unexpected.

    o If people are used to hearing news via a memo, try face-to-face or video next time.

- Know that it is better to give too much information than too little.

- Hold impromptu meetings in the office, which should be short. If you don't have new information, encourage questions, which may uncover issues you are not aware of.

- Keep a flipchart or whiteboard in your work area.

    o Write news on it regularly.

    o Allow your employees to record questions that they want to deal with at your meetings.

- If you don't give information to your employees, they will at best speculate what's going on, at worst, they will make it up and tell others. Take a look at what happens when you withhold information:

Manager (that's you!) Thinks	Employees Think
It's too early to tell them.	Silence must mean it's pretty bad.
This news is too frightening; we'd better wait.	We're going through reorganization.
I'm afraid if we tell them, productivity will drop.	The company's going belly-up. Where else can I get a job?

Step #6: Set a Postive Communication Tone

Employees will follow your lead whether you realize it or not.

You have the power to influence the attitude of the team simply through the delivery of your communications. By setting a positive tone, you will increase the likelihood of having your employees make suggestions and offer up ideas.

When you can create this two-way dialogue, you will be setting the foundation for a strong, committed team.

- Encourage communication from your employees.
- Manage by walking around.
    - Be visible.
    - Maintain an open-door policy.
- Listen to what employees are telling you.
    - Listen to understand rather than to rebut.
    - Listen to their thoughts as well as their feelings. This demonstrates respect and will encourage further idea sharing.
- Ask for employees' opinions. This gesture makes employees feel valued and it can have a positive impact on their commitment.
- Encourage employees' ideas by setting up suggestion systems, performance improvement teams, focus groups, and communication sessions.
- Act on these ideas to encourage involvement. If you can't act, explain why not as soon as possible.
- Thank employees for their suggestions, even if you don't always agree with them. Challenge yourself to think of how the idea could work rather than why it might not.
- If you are not clear about an idea you are listening to, repeat it in your own words. This will reinforce your understanding and demonstrate your interest.
- Don't just tell your employees what to do - explain the reasons behind it.

Tips to Making the Shift from Peer to Boss

Step #1: Establish your authority deftly

- To exert authority effectively in your new role, walk a fine line between under-doing and over-doing control.
    - Don't act as "super-peer."
    - Don't develop Napoleon complex and begin issuing edicts.
    - Don't implement plans to create a new work culture right away. Put them on hold for a while.
- When you do want to implement changes, do it gradually.
- Use a "consult-and-decide" style for dealing with key issues for the first few months
    - This will help establish your own authority.
    - Listen and consider carefully, then make and thoroughly communicate decisions.
- Once you have established a new rhythm with your team, engage in more consensus building if and when it's appropriate.

Step #2: Focus on what's good for your university or the work unit

- Some former peers, now direct reports, may worry that your promotion heralds the installation of a new regime.
    - Early on, they may be hyper-vigilant to see if you will play favorites.
    - Political or hidden agendas will undermine your leadership.
- Focus on doing what is right for the organization or the unit. Being clear that the welfare of others matters most to you will help alleviate this issue.
- The sooner your new direct reports see that you will be "hard on the issues and soft on the people," the better.
- Have a fair process for making key decisions. This includes establishing and upholding work processes that are perceived as fair.

Step#3: Rethink what you delegate

- In the early 1950's Peter Drucker said the ability to delegate lies at the heart of leadership. As a new manager delegation will be a key challenge.

- Reassure people that you will delegate appropriately, not dump on them.

- It's essential that you take a step back and figure out what you need to delegate before deciding how.

- The types of things you delegate will most likely differ depending on your level in the organization and how many people are in the organization:
    - If you supervise six people it makes sense to delegate specific tasks.
    - At 60 people, your focus has to shift from tasks to projects and processes.

Step #4: Communicate, communicate, and communicate

- The good news about moving up is you get a broader view of your university and more scope to shape it.

- The bad news is you are further from the front lines and more likely to receive filtered info.
    - Your former peers will share info differently with you now that you are boss.
    - Employees may start to shield you from information that you would have received in the past.
    - To avoid this, work to establish a climate of trust, openness and a culture of "no surprises." Making this work requires that you don't punish people for sharing bad news, and that you don't require them to have iron-clad answers when they bring problems.

- Because peers will most likely share information differently, you'll need to look for different ways to figure out what is going on at the front lines of your university.
    - Engage in regular direct contact with customers and front-line employees; provide direct channels for raising serious concerns.
    - Do this in way that doesn't undermine the integrity of your management hierarchy.

Step #5 Re-enlist your (good) former peers

- For every "winner" who gets promoted, there are likely to be one or more "losers" who wanted the job but didn't get it.

- Newly-promoted supervisors typically have to deal with the fact that some former peers may be deeply disappointed, angry or nurse bad feelings.

- If direct reports can't or won't get over disappointment, try these tips:
    - Help them find opportunities within their current job to shift negative energy.
    - Recognize their career prospects. They may fear that their careers have been dead-ended. Address their concerns.
    - Show respect and focus on past impact/contributions they made to the organization.
    - Take opportunities to recognize their individual contributions.

- Disappointed former peers experience a process akin to Kubler-Ross stages of grieving
    - These stages are denial, anger, bargaining, depression and acceptance.
    - Know that it can take some time for them to work things through.

- Think hard about when and how to best engage with disappointed direct reports - early or later on, directly or obliquely, empathetically or matter-of-factly.

Step #6: Re-think your own advice and counsel network

- Have a network of people who can provide advice and counsel.

- The more senior you are, the more likely it is that you need sophisticated and supportive political advisers/mentors in your network.

- The advice and counsel network you had before your promotion may need to change if your technical or soft skills have changed drastically. If necessary, re-engineer your relationships with existing advisers and counselors to focus on new topics.

Step #7: Recognize that relationships have to change.

In the process of working together and facing challenges, some former peers may have become close friends. Accept that one price of promotion is for relationships with former peers to become less personal. The unfortunate reality is that close personal relationships and effective supervisory relationships are rarely compatible.

Meet with your friends and tell them that some things have to change.

- ✓ *Stay professional:*
    - o You can't afford to have judgment about issues clouded by personal feelings.
    - o You can't allow the perception that you play favorites.
    - o Don't treat your friends any better or worse than anyone else.
    - o Tell all employees that you will be fair with your evaluations.

- ✓ *Evaluate performance fairly:*
    - o You could find that you need to deliver hard-edged performance feedback, yet you desire to cushion the hurt.
    - o If you succumb to the temptation to go easy, you'll undermine the performance of the new organization and your own leadership.
    - o In reality, an evaluation is nothing more than a fact-based summary of issues that you should have been addressing all along anyway, so there shouldn't be any awkward surprises.

- ✓ *Socializing:*
    - o It's okay to remain a part of your team's social group, as long as socializing is in the normal course of business.
    - o If people go out for happy hour or play softball together you can participate, but don't spend *too* much time with old friends outside of work.
    - o Don't give employees an inside scoop on what's happening with higher-ups.
    - o Don't participate in gossip.

CSU Supervisory Development Toolkit

For additional information on topics covered in this Learning Guide, go to
https://csyou.calstate.edu then navigate to:

Divisions & Organizations > HR > SPD > Talent Management Toolkits

---

Change Management
Toolkit

Performance Management
Toolkit

Principles of Supervision
Toolkit

   Managing Performance &
   Developing Direct Reports

   Guiding and Organizing the
   Work

   Managing Relationships

   Managing Yourself

Recruitment Toolkit

Workforce Planning Toolkit

Principles of Supervision

As a supervisor, you have a profound impact on your employees and the work environment. Your actions can also indirectly affect others as the people you supervise might one day lead teams themselves.

This toolkit provides tools and resources to help you improve the performance and commitment of your staff *and yourself*. It's targeted to managers who are new in role, or who might need a quick refresher.

Start learning how *you* can be an excellent supervisor by:

- Examining the core differences and similarities between leaders and managers
- Reading the Stephen J Drotter & Ram Charan article "Building Leaders at Every Level: A Leadership Pipeline"
- Accessing the "Principles of Supervision Learning Guide" available on Amazon.

If you have any questions or suggestions to improve this toolkit, please contact Systemwide Professional Development and let us know!

Supervisor Success Factors

Click on each success factor for more details and resources

 Managing **PERFORMANCE**

 Developing **DIRECT REPORTS**

 Guiding & Organizing **THE WORK**

 Managing **RELATIONSHIPS**

 Managing **YOURSELF**

Recommended Reading

- Connors, R. and Smith, T. (2010) *The Oz Principle: Getting Results Through Individual and Organizational Accountability*

- Eichinger, R.W. and Lombardo M.M. (year) *FYI: For Your Improvement, A Development and Coaching Guide*

- Kouzes, J.M. and Posner, B.Z. (2012) *The Leadership Challenge: How to Make Extraordinary Things Happen in Organizations*

- Lencioni, P. (2002) *The Five Dysfunctions of a Team: A Leadership Fable*

- Watkins, M. (2013) *The First 90 days: Proven Strategies for Getting Up to Speed Faster and Smarter*

Action Plan

Name: _____ **Campus:** _____ **Date:** _____

Insights What important things did you learn?	Development Actions What actions do you plan to take?	Accountability Who else needs to be involved and how?	Start Date What is a reasonable time to work on this action?

Insights What important things did you learn?	Development Actions What actions do you plan to take?	Accountability Who else needs to be involved and how?	Due Date What is a reasonable time to complete this action?

Insights What important things did you learn?	Development Actions What actions do you plan to take?	Accountability Who else needs to be involved and how?	Due Date What is a reasonable time to complete this action?

Insights What important things did you learn?	Development Actions What actions do you plan to take?	Accountability Who else needs to be involved and how?	Due Date What is a reasonable time to complete this action?

24965822R00071

Made in the USA
San Bernardino, CA
08 February 2019